STAR WARS
X-WING
ROGUE SQUADRON

the warrior princess

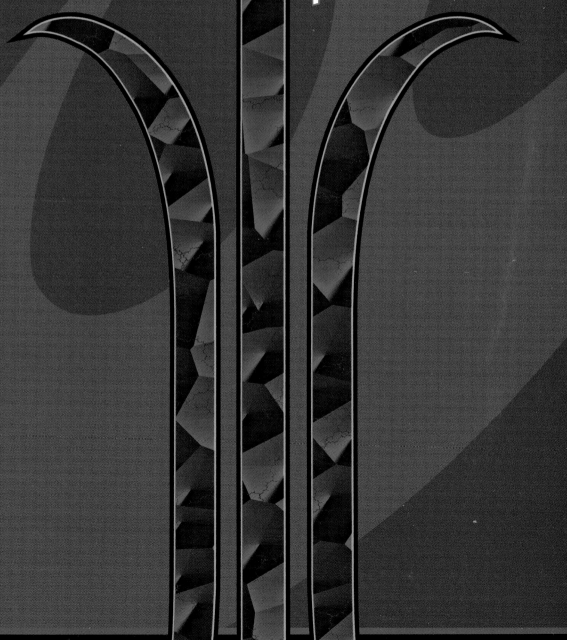

STAR WARS
X-WING
ROGUE SQUADRON

the WARRIOR PRINCESS

Michael A. Stackpole
story

Scott Tolson
script

John Nadeau
pencils

Jordi Ensign
inks

Dave Nestelle
colors

Vickie Williams
letters

John K. Snyder III
cover

TITAN BOOKS

Mike Richardson
publisher

Peet Janes
series editor

Suzanne Taylor and **Chris Warner**
collection editors

Corey Stephens
collection designer

Special thanks to Allan Kausch and Lucy Autrey Wilson at Lucas Licensing.

Neil Hankerson • executive vice president
Andy Karabatsos • vice president & controller
Randy Stradley • director of editorial
Cindy Marks • director of production & design
Mark Cox • art director
Sean Tierney • computer graphics director
Michael Martens • director of sales & marketing
Tod Borleske • director of licensing
David Scroggy • product development
Dale LaFountain • director of m.i.s.
Kim Haines • director of human resources
Ken Lizzi • general counsel

Published by Titan Books Ltd. by arrangement with Dark Horse Comics, Inc.

This book collects issues one through four of the Dark Horse comic-book series
Star Wars: X-Wing Rogue Squadron — The Warrior Princess.

Published by
Titan Books Ltd.
42-44 Dolben Street
London SE1 0UP

First edition: November 1998
ISBN: 1-85286-997-6

1 3 5 7 9 10 8 6 4 2

Printed in Canada

NOW!

ALL RIGHT, ROGUE SQUADRON, YOU KNOW THE DRILL-- SHAKE 'EM AND BAKE 'EM!

HOBBIE KLIVAN

COPY THAT, ROGUE LEADER!

LT. WES JANSON

...NOTHING ON MY SCANNERS AND THEN...COPY THAT, BOSS!

PLLR NEP

AFFIRMATIVE, ROGUE LEADER! BLAST 'EM!

PLOURR ILO

WAAAHOOO!!!

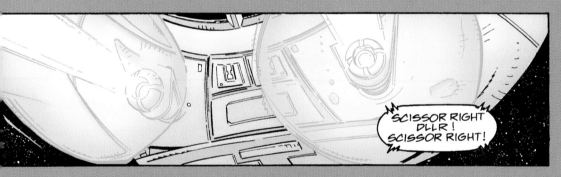

YOU SEE THAT, HOBBIE? THEY GOT DLLR!

I SAW IT! NOTHING WE CAN DO ABOUT IT NOW!

JANSON, BREAK OFF! GET OUT OF THERE!

JANSON, DO YOU COPY? BREAK OFF! YOU HAVE TWO EYES ON YA!

TIME FOR SOME PAYBACK, HOBBIE! THIS ONE'S FOR...

GAAAK!!

WES!!

ROGUE LEADER, I'VE LOST MY REAR DEFLECTOR! I--

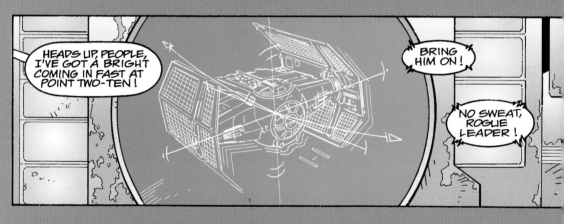

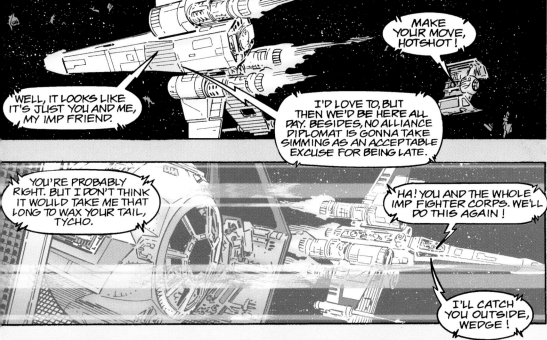

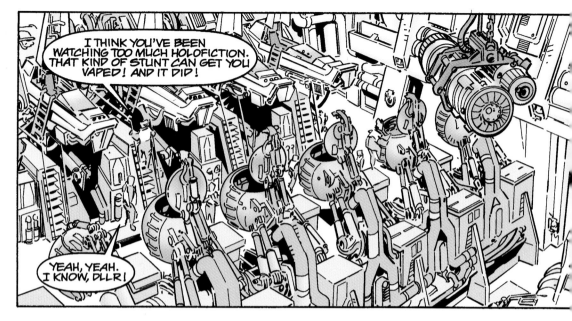

I THINK YOU'VE BEEN WATCHING TOO MUCH HOLOFICTION. THAT KIND OF STUNT CAN GET YOU VAPED! AND IT DID!

YEAH, YEAH. I KNOW, DLLR!

YEAH! WHO RIGGED THE SIMULATOR SEATS WITH AN ELECTRICAL CHARGE, ANYWAY? THAT WAS SOME ZAP!

I FELT THE SENSATION TO BE... EXHILARAT- ING!

IT'S JUST WHEN I HEARD YOU SCREAM, SIMULATOR OR NOT, YOU SOUNDED LIKE YOU WERE REALLY HURT. NOW I KNOW WHAT MADE YOU DO THAT.

I'VE GOT AN IDEA!

YEAH, YOU WOULD, NRIN!

UM...WELL... IT WAS ME.

ACTING ON WEDGE'S ORDERS, OF COURSE.

YOU!!??

HA! I KNEW IT!

YOU SEE, WEDGE BELIEVED THAT THE SIMULATOR LACKED THE PROPER AMOUNT OF REALISM FOR SUCH BATTLE-HARDENED VETERANS AS OURSELVES.

HE FELT THAT A BIT OF EXTRA SIMULATION WAS REQUIRED TO BRIN[G] ABOUT THE PROPER RESPONSE.

AND I CONCURRED.

AH, HERE THEY ARE NOW, GRAND DUKE.

CAPTAIN WEDGE ANTILLES, MAY I PRESENT THE GRAND DUKE GROR PERNON.

AN HONOR, SIR. MAY I PRESENT ONE OF MY OFFICERS, LT. TYCHO CELCHU.

MY LORD.

THIS IS POE, THE GRAND DUKE'S PROTOCOL DROID.

WELL, SHALL WE BEGIN, GENTLEMEN? GRAND DUKE.

GENTLEMEN, MY WORLD, EIATTU, IS DYING. A CANCER IS EATING AWAY AT ITS VERY HEART. OUR PEOPLE ARE KILLING EACH OTHER.

WE NEED TO BE MADE WHOLE.

MY WORLD IS A TROUBLED ONE. IT HAS ALWAYS BEEN THUS.

YEARS AGO, WITH THE FALL OF THE OLD REPUBLIC, MY BROTHER, EMPEROR ANTBBIANPLOURR III, BARTERED AWAY OUR PRIDE AND OUR HONOR TO KEEP THE THRONE, AND THE IMPERIALS FROM OUR WORLD.

THIS WAS THE BEGINNING OF THE END FOR US.

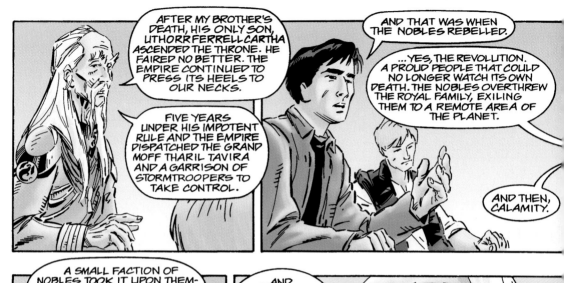

AFTER MY BROTHER'S DEATH, HIS ONLY SON, UTHORR FERRELL CARTHA ASCENDED THE THRONE. HE FAIRED NO BETTER. THE EMPIRE CONTINUED TO PRESS ITS HEELS TO OUR NECKS.

FIVE YEARS UNDER HIS IMPOTENT RULE AND THE EMPIRE DISPATCHED THE GRAND MOFF THARIL TAVIRA AND A GARRISON OF STORMTROOPERS TO TAKE CONTROL.

AND THAT WAS WHEN THE NOBLES REBELLED.

...YES, THE REVOLUTION. A PROUD PEOPLE THAT COULD NO LONGER WATCH ITS OWN DEATH. THE NOBLES OVERTHREW THE ROYAL FAMILY, EXILING THEM TO A REMOTE AREA OF THE PLANET.

AND THEN, CALAMITY.

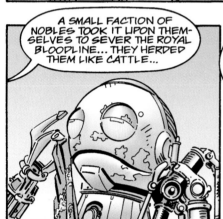

A SMALL FACTION OF NOBLES TOOK IT UPON THEM-SELVES TO SEVER THE ROYAL BLOODLINE... THEY HERDED THEM LIKE CATTLE...

...AND SLAUGHTERED THE ROYAL FAMILY. MY NEPHEW AND HIS CHILDREN. ALL DEAD.

OR SO WE THOUGHT.

IMPERIAL INVESTIGATORS CONFIRMED THE DEATHS, IDENTIFYING ALL THE BODIES SAVE THAT OF THE YOUNGEST PRINCESS AND THE PRINCE.

WHEN WE HEARD THIS, WE THOUGHT IT A CRUEL TRICK PLAYED BY THE IMPERIALS.

THAT IS UNTIL LAST MONTH, WHEN PRINCE HARRANDATHA RETURNED.

WHAT?

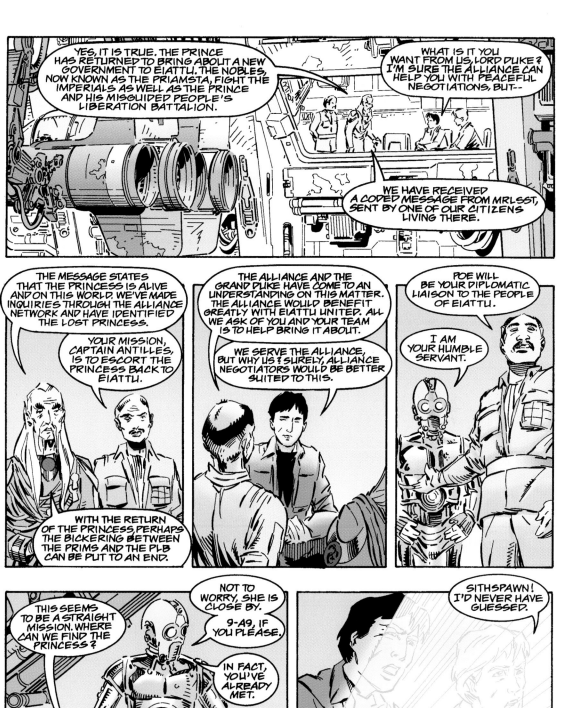

YES, IT IS TRUE. THE PRINCE HAS RETURNED TO BRING ABOUT A NEW GOVERNMENT TO EIATTU. THE NOBLES, NOW KNOWN AS THE PRIAMSTA, FIGHT THE IMPERIALS AS WELL AS THE PRINCE AND HIS MISGUIDED PEOPLE'S LIBERATION BATTALION.

WHAT IS IT YOU WANT FROM US, LORD DUKE? I'M SURE THE ALLIANCE CAN HELP YOU WITH PEACEFUL NEGOTIATIONS, BUT--

WE HAVE RECEIVED A CODED MESSAGE FROM MRLSST, SENT BY ONE OF OUR CITIZENS LIVING THERE.

THE MESSAGE STATES THAT THE PRINCESS IS ALIVE AND ON THIS WORLD. WE'VE MADE INQUIRIES THROUGH THE ALLIANCE NETWORK AND HAVE IDENTIFIED THE LOST PRINCESS.

YOUR MISSION, CAPTAIN ANTILLES, IS TO ESCORT THE PRINCESS BACK TO EIATTU.

WITH THE RETURN OF THE PRINCESS, PERHAPS THE BICKERING BETWEEN THE PRIMS AND THE PLB CAN BE PUT TO AN END.

THE ALLIANCE AND THE GRAND DUKE HAVE COME TO AN UNDERSTANDING ON THIS MATTER. THE ALLIANCE WOULD BENEFIT GREATLY WITH EIATTU UNITED. ALL WE ASK OF YOU AND YOUR TEAM IS TO HELP BRING IT ABOUT.

WE SERVE THE ALLIANCE, BUT WHY US? SURELY, ALLIANCE NEGOTIATORS WOULD BE BETTER SUITED TO THIS.

POE WILL BE YOUR DIPLOMATIC LIAISON TO THE PEOPLE OF EIATTU.

I AM YOUR HUMBLE SERVANT.

THIS SEEMS TO BE A STRAIGHT MISSION. WHERE CAN WE FIND THE PRINCESS?

NOT TO WORRY, SHE IS CLOSE BY.

9-A9, IF YOU PLEASE.

IN FACT, YOU'VE ALREADY MET.

SITHSPAWN! I'D NEVER HAVE GUESSED.

NOR I. IF YOU'LL FOLLOW ME, GENTLEMEN.

SHE HAS A POINT, NRIN, THE X-WING IS A DATED SHIP.

DAMN RIGHT I HAVE A POINT! THE X-WING IS OBSOLETE! THE B-WING IS THE FUTURE OF SPACE COMBAT.

I'LL NOT HEAR ANY MORE OF THESE FOUL SLANDERS AGAINST A GALLANT SHIP THAT HAS DISTINGUISHED ITSELF IN BATTLE AFTER BATTLE!

OR HAVE YOU FORGOTTEN THAT IT WAS AN X-WING THAT DESTROYED THE FIRST DEATH STAR SINGLE-HANDED! OBSOLETE, INDEED!

OH, DON'T BE SO MELODRAMATIC! SURE AN X-WING DESTROYED THE DEATH STAR, BUT THAT X-WING HAD A GREAT PILOT AT THE CONTROLS, WITH THE FORCE AS HIS CO-PILOT.

WOW, LOOK AT 'EM GO AT IT.

YEAH, THEY'RE EITHER GOING TO KILL EACH OTHER, OR TAKE THE UNION VOW.

RIDICULOUS! UTTER NONSENSE! THE X-WING INDEED. SILLY LOOKING THING!

HA! THE B-WING'S AS OLD AS MYNOCK DROPPINGS! AND JUST A LITTLE MORE USEFUL!

IF THE X-WING DIDN'T HAVE THAT BLIND SPOT AT THE REAR OF ITS BELLY, OUR OWN CAPTAIN MIGHT HAVE TAKEN OUT THE DEATH STAR! THE B-WING HAS NO BLIND SPOT!

I GIVE IT A WEEK BEFORE--

--EXCUSE ME, FEYLIS.

WHAT ARE YOU DOING HERE?

PRINCESS ISPLOURRDACARTHA ESTILLO, YOUR PRESENCE STRENGTHENS AN OLD MAN'S HEART.

I CAN FIX THAT.

Eiattu.

THE BUSINESS OF LIFE GOES ON HERE. MOST OF THE LIFE FORMS THAT INHABIT THIS SMALL PLANET CARE NOTHING ABOUT EMPIRES, ALLIANCES, OR WAR.

YET FOR THE ONES THAT DO, TONIGHT IS A NIGHT THAT HAS TAKEN TOO MANY YEARS TO ARRIVE. TONIGHT THEIR PRINCESS HAS RETURNED, AND SHE HAS BROUGHT A GIFT FOR HER PEOPLE.

A GIFT THAT WAS TAKEN FROM THEM A LONG TIME AGO. A GIFT FOR THEM TO PLANT INSIDE THEIR HEARTS AND TREASURE LIKE GOLD.

SHE HAS BROUGHT WITH HER... HOPE.

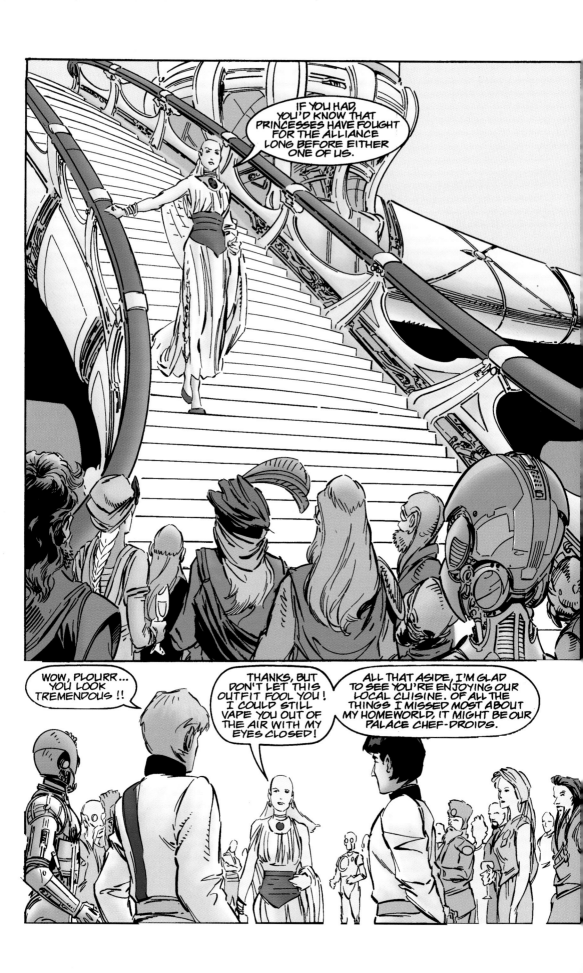

WELL, I SEE NOW THAT THERE'S A LOT THAT YOU'D MISS ABOUT THIS PLACE! IF WE HAVE A CHANCE, I'D LIKE TO BAG ONE OF THOSE THUVASAURS I SAW WANDERING AROUND WHEN I LANDED!

OF COURSE, BUT I THINK YOU'LL FIND THAT EIATTU HAS A LOT MORE TO OFFER THAN SAURIAN-HUNTING! BUT LET'S NOT FORGET WHY WE'RE HERE! THIS IS A BEAUTIFUL WORLD, GENTLEMEN--

--AND I WILL NOT ALLOW THE EMPIRE'S PRESENCE TO INFECT IT ANY LONGER.

SPOKEN LIKE A TRUE PRINCESS...

A PRINCESS THAT CAN PULL THE EARS OFF A GLINDARK.

PRESENTING THE PRINCESS ISPLOURRDACARTHA, EMPRESS APPARENT-HEIR TO THE ROYAL HOUSE! LONG MAY SHE REIGN!

LONG MAY SHE REIGN!

SO TELL ME, WHICH LIFE DO YOU PREFER, PRINCESS OR PILOT?

DIFFICULT QUESTION. I WAS BORN ONE, BUT MADE MYSELF INTO THE OTHER. I'VE SPENT SO MUCH OF MY LIFE FIGHTING, I CAN HARDLY REMEMBER WHAT THIS LIFE IS LIKE.

IT WOULD BE TOO MUCH TO HOPE YOU WOULD REMEMBER ME, ISPLOURRDACARTHA.

WHY NO, I'M AFRAID I DON'T. YOU ARE?

COUNT RIAL PERNON.

RIAL...AH, YES, I DO RECALL...IF YOU WILL EXCUSE ME.

SHE IS BEAUTIFUL, IS SHE NOT? EVEN MORE BEAUTIFUL THAN I REMEMBER...

SHE CERTAINLY IS...UH...I'M WEDGE ANTILLES.

PRIVILEGED TO MEET YOU. HOW DO YOU KNOW THE PRINCESS?

I'M HER COMMANDING OFFICER. HOW DO YOU KNOW HER?

I AM HER SECOND COUSIN. WE GREW UP TOGETHER.

I DO ADMIT, I AM A LITTLE DISAPPOINTED IN HER REACTION. YOU WOULD THINK SHE WOULD BE HAPPIER TO SEE HER FUTURE HUSBAND...

THAT SO? I THOUGHT THE DEWBACK FAMILY WAS ONLY NATIVE TO DRY WORLDS, LIKE TATOOINE OR BREEKA.

AND THE DEWBACK IS DOCILE TO A FAULT! THEY WOULDN'T HURT A--

--BUT A THUVASAUR WOULD!

THE STABLE MASTER SAYS THAT THE THUVASAURS WERE TRANSPORTED TO EIATTU SPECIFICALLY FOR SPORT. APPARENTLY THEY ADAPT QUICKLY TO HARSH ENVIRONMENTS.

IN A MATTER OF TIME THEY HAD DESTROYED THE LOCAL PREDATORS AND MOVED TO THE TOP OF THE FOOD CHAIN.

THE THUVASAURS WENT FROM BEING TAME, DOMESTIC ANIMALS TO COLD-BLOODED PREDATORS.

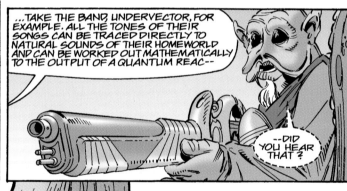

...TAKE THE BAND, UNDERVECTOR, FOR EXAMPLE. ALL THE TONES OF THEIR SONGS CAN BE TRACED DIRECTLY TO NATURAL SOUNDS OF THEIR HOMEWORLD AND CAN BE WORKED OUT MATHEMATICALLY TO THE OUTPUT OF A QUANTUM REAC--

--DID YOU HEAR THAT?

DLLR, YOU HAVEN'T HEARD A WORD I'VE SAID!

DLLR, ARE YOU LISTENING TO ME?

OF COURSE I'M LISTENING TO YOU! WITH EARS LIKE MINE, YOU THINK I HAVE TROUBLE HEARING THINGS?

DLLR, WHAT'S THE MATTER? WHY ARE YOU SO JUMPY?

DO YOU KNOW WHAT THOSE THUVASAURS CAN DO? WE WALK INTO THIS FORCE-FORSAKEN SWAMP WITH NO GUIDE AND NO TRACKING DEVICES, AND YOU ASK ME WHY I'M SO JUMPY?

BESIDES, I KEEP HEARING SOMETHING JUST OUT OF EARSHOT AND I CAN'T MAKE IT OUT.

AND AS FOR UNDERVECTOR'S MUSIC, THEY STINK LIKE TAUNTAUN DROPPINGS!

CAN YOU BELIEVE IT? PLOURR A PRINCESS, AND NOT ONE OF HER CREWMATES SUSPECTED!

I SAW THE NOBILITY IN HER EYES FROM THE MOMENT I MET HER.

SUCH TRAGEDY IN PLOURR'S LIFE. HER FAMILY KILLED, A LIFE ON THE RUN IN FEAR OF SOMEONE DISCOVERING HER TRUE IDENTITY. AND NOW--

UMM, NRIN? WHY ARE YOU WEARING THAT HAT?

IT'S PART OF THE TRADITIONAL HUNTING UNIFORM OF THE EIATTU NOBLES. THEY'VE WORN IT FOR GENERATIONS...

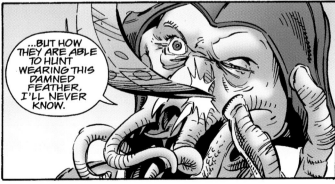

...BUT HOW THEY ARE ABLE TO HUNT WEARING THIS DAMNED FEATHER, I'LL NEVER KNOW.

FROM WHAT WEDGE TELLS ME, COUNT PERNON AND PLOURR WERE BETROTHED WHEN THEY WERE CHILDREN.

IN THE EYES OF THE STATE THEY'RE MARRIED, BUT PLOURR DOESN'T QUITE SEE IT THAT WAY.

WITH ALL THAT'S HAPPENED, THE FIGHTING WITH THE NOBLES, HER BROTHER HARRAN LEADING THE PLB...I THINK THE LAST THING PLOURR NEEDS IS A HUSBAND. EVEN IF HE IS A COUNT.

IF I KNOW PLOURR, SHE CAN HANDLE IT... EVEN IF SHE NEEDS TO KICK A LITTLE--

HEY, JANSON!!!

THERE'S SOMETHING GOING ON IN THERE. I'M HEARING SOME STRANGE STUFF...

YOU GOT THAT RIGHT.

I THOUGHT THE STABLE KEEPER TOLD YOU THUVASAURS DIDN'T LIKE THE DEEPER SWAMPS...

MAYBE IT'S SOMETHING ELSE. I--

YOU HEAR THAT?

WHATTA YA' GOT, DLLR?

BLASTER FIRE... AND IF I'M NOT MISTAKEN, BLASTER FIRE WITH AN IMP RING TO IT.

LET'S CHECK IT OUT.

MAY NOT BE AS GOOD AS A THUVASAUR PELT, BUT AN IMP HIDE'LL DO.

SON OF A JUMPING--

THIS IS THE SITE OF THE LAST PEOPLE'S LIBERATION BATTALION ATTACK.

HOW MANY WERE INJURED, COUNT PERNON?

FIFTEEN GUARDS AND AN IMPERIAL BANKER. THE ATTACK HAPPENED DURING THE TRANSPORT OF THE IMPERIAL PAYROLL, SO THERE WERE NO CIVILIANS IN THE AREA.

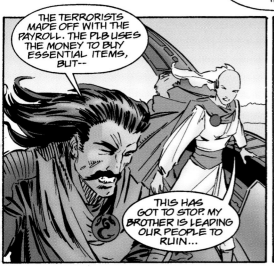

THE TERRORISTS MADE OFF WITH THE PAYROLL. THE PLB USES THE MONEY TO BUY ESSENTIAL ITEMS, BUT--

THIS HAS GOT TO STOP. MY BROTHER IS LEADING OUR PEOPLE TO RUIN...

WEDGE HERE.

≷SQUAWK≷ WE'VE STEPPED INTO SOMETHING AWFUL DEEP HERE! A BUZZZER S'NEST OF IMPS HAVE US PINNED DOWN!!

THEY'RE ALL OVER US, WEDGE! WE CAN'T HOLD OFF THE TROOPERS *AND* THE TIES!

HOLD TIGHT, JANSON!! WE'RE ON OUR WAY!

COUNT PERNON, YOU'VE GOT TO GET US TO OUR X-WINGS! MY PEOPLE ARE IN TROUBLE!!

YOUR COMRADES MUST HAVE COME ACROSS AN IMPERIAL PATROL LOOKING FOR PLB ENCAMPMENTS.

ARE THEY ALL RIGHT?

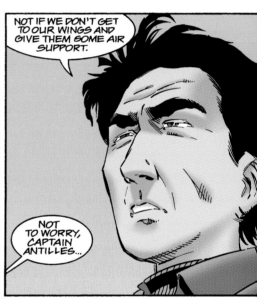

NOT IF WE DON'T GET TO OUR WINGS AND GIVE THEM SOME AIR SUPPORT.

NOT TO WORRY, CAPTAIN ANTILLES...

I SHALL HASTEN OUR PACE.

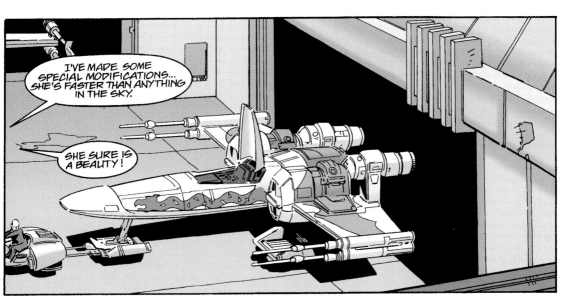

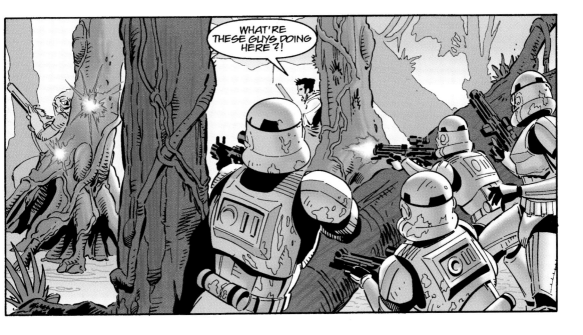

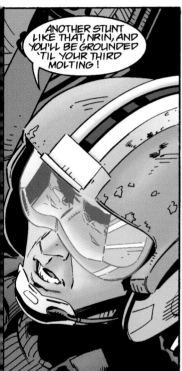

ANOTHER STUNT LIKE THAT, NRIN, AND YOU'LL BE GROUNDED 'TIL YOUR THIRD MOLTING!

NOW, GET SOME COVER!

YES SIR, CAPTAIN ANTILLES, SIR!!

RIAL, GET OUT OF THERE! YOU'VE GOT TWO ON YOUR TAIL!

NOT TO WORRY, MY PRINCESS. I HAVE THEM RIGHT WHERE I WANT THEM.

FOR THE PRIDE OF EIATTU!

WOW, WHOEVER'S IN THAT Z-95 SURE HAS GUTS TO PULL A SILERIAN STALL IN THAT CRATE.

WE GOTTA GET SOMEBODY ON THEIR FLANK, JANSON! WE'RE GETTING POUNDED--

LOOKS LIKE YOU GOT YOUR WISH, HOBBIE!!

LIBERATION!!!

WONDERFUL, AN ENEMY OF THE EMPIRE IS AN ALLY OF OURS. COME, OUR CAMP IS NEARBY, MY COMMANDER WILL WISH TO HAVE A WORD WITH YOU.

THAT WAS *SOME* FLYING, COUNT PERNON! I THOUGHT THOSE EYEBALLS HAD YOU COLD.

I THINK HE'D EVEN GIVE YOU A RUN, PLOURR... I MEAN, PRINCESS ISPLOURRDACARTHA...

I WAS ONLY PERFORMING MY DUTY TO MY WORLD AND PRINCESS.

COME NOW, COUNT PERNON. YOUR SKILL IN FLIGHT DOES THE THRONE PROUD.

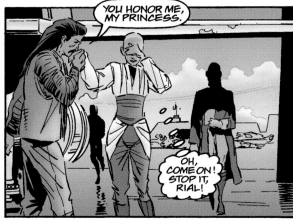

YOU HONOR ME, MY PRINCESS.

OH, COME ON! STOP IT, RIAL!

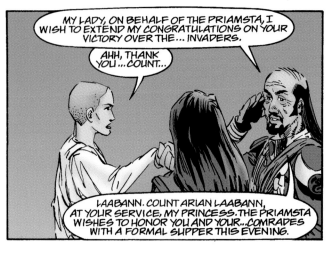

MY LADY, ON BEHALF OF THE PRIAMSTA, I WISH TO EXTEND MY CONGRATULATIONS ON YOUR VICTORY OVER THE... INVADERS.

AHH, THANK YOU ...COUNT...

LAABANN. COUNT ARIAN LAABANN, AT YOUR SERVICE, MY PRINCESS. THE PRIAMSTA WISHES TO HONOR YOU AND YOUR...COMRADES WITH A FORMAL SUPPER THIS EVENING.

WE WOULD BE HONORED!

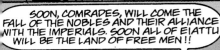

COME, HARRAN WILL WANT TO MEET WITH YOU.

COMRADE HARRAN, THIS IS LT. JANSON OF THE REBEL ALLIANCE AND HIS CREWMATES OF ROGUE SQUADRON!

WELCOME, MY FRIENDS! WELCOME TO FREELAND!

THANK YOU, SIR, IT IS AN HONOR!

YOU ARE WELCOME TO EAT WITH US. WE HAVE PLENTY OF THE BEST FOOD, DRINK, AND CREDITS THE EMPIRE HAS TO OFFER!

HE'S QUITE A LEADER.

A LEADER WITH BEAUTIFUL EYES!

HMMP.

AS SOON AS OUR OTHER PATROLS REPORT IN, I WILL LEAD YOU BACK TO THE CITY. BUT FOR NOW, GOOD FOOD AND FINE SONG.

TELL ME, LT. JANSON...

...WHAT CAN YOU TELL ME OF MY DARLING SISTER?

I SEE THE FUTURE OF EIATTU AS COLD, DARK, AND HATEFUL!

A FUTURE WHERE THE GOOD PEOPLE OF EIATTU ARE POISONED BY THE HYPOCRISY OF THE NOBLE CLASS.

...WHAT!??

...WHAT!??

A POISON THAT HAS A SWEET SCENT, BUT IS DEADLY TO THE TASTE!

UH, OH...

...ISPLOURRDACARTHA... PLEASE...

GENTLEMEN, EIATTU WILL NOT DRINK THIS POISON!

HAVE A CARE, PRINCESS, FOR WITHOUT THE PRIAMSTA YOU HAVE NO HOPE OF DEFEATING THE PEOPLE'S LIBERATION BATTALION!

CALM YOURSELF, LAABANN...

I DON'T KNOW IF THIS WAS SUCH A GOOD IDEA, HOBBIE. I CAN'T REACH WEDGE ON THE COMLINK TO REPORT IN.

TAKE IT EASY, WES! WE'LL CAMP HERE TONIGHT AND HEAD FOR THE CITY IN THE MORNING.

BESIDES, WE CAME OUT HERE FOR SOME R AND R, AND THAT'S WHAT WE'RE GETTING, RIGHT?

YEAH, AT EASE, WES! ROGUE SQUADRON NEVER HAD IT SO GOOD. I'M SURE WEDGE AND TYCHO ARE HAVING A FINE TIME SLEEPING IN THE PALACE!

SGT. ASHAAD, WILL HARRAN BE JOINING US FOR A DRINK?

OUR GREAT LEADER HAS GONE ON RECONNAISSANCE. HE SHOULD RETURN BY DAYBREAK TO LEAD YOU BACK TO THE CITY.

SEE, WE'LL LEAVE BY FIRST LIGHT! HAVE A DRINK!

OKAY. I GUESS YOU'RE RIGHT.

TO THE GOOD LIFE!

YAAAAAAHHH

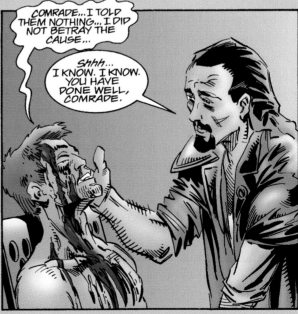

SOME OF HER EARLIEST MEMORIES ARE OF FLYING.

THE SENSATION WOULD LAST FOR ONLY A SECOND, BUT IT SENT SUCH A RUSH THROUGH THE YOUNG GIRL. SHE WAS NEVER AFRAID, BUT ALWAYS EXHILARATED, BECAUSE SHE KNEW HER FATHER WAS ALWAYS THERE TO CATCH HER.

NOTHING IN HER YOUNG LIFE MADE HER FEEL AS GOOD.

FOR MOST OF HER ADULT LIFE, PLOURR HAS BEEN FLYING, BUT NOW THE SENSATION IS DIFFERENT. SHE HAS BECOME A FIERCE WARRIOR AND PILOT WITHOUT PEER, BLASTING HER FOES OUT OF THE AIR...

...ALL THE WHILE, WISHING FOR THE DEATHS OF THE MEN WHO BUTCHERED HER FAMILY.

YEEEEHAAA!

NOW SHE'S RETURNED TO HER HOMEWORLD, AS SHE KNEW IN HER HEART SHE WOULD HAVE TO SOMEDAY...EVEN THOUGH NO ONE WOULD BE THERE TO CATCH HER.

THAT IS, UNTIL NOW.

YOU RIDE WELL, MY COUNT! NOT MANY CAN KEEP UP WITH ME WHEN I GET GOING!!

SO I SEE! I WOULD NOT HAVE THOUGHT THAK-RIDING TO BE A REQUIREMENT OF ALLIANCE FLIGHT TRAINING!

IT'S NOT, IN FACT, I HAVEN'T EVEN SEEN A THAK SINCE I WAS A CHILD.

BUT... I GUESS SOME THINGS YOU JUST DON'T FORGET...

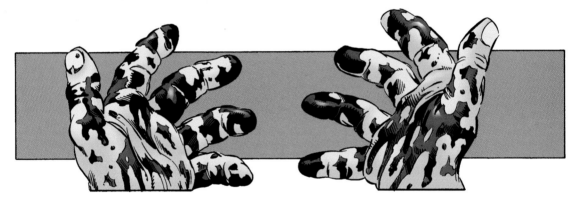

...NO MATTER HOW HARD YOU TRY.

PRINCESS... PLOURR. I WANT YOU TO KNOW HOW ASHAMED I AM OF THE ROLE MY FATHER PLAYED IN THE DEATH OF YOUR FAMILY. HE--

YOUR FATHER WAS NOT RESPONSIBLE, RIAL. IN FACT, HE TRIED TO PREVENT IT. THERE IS NO SHAME ON YOUR HOUSE.

NOR ON YOU, MY COUNT.

PERHAPS. I ONLY WISHED TO EASE THE PAIN OF YOUR RETURN IN SOME SMALL WAY. IT MUST BE DIFFICULT FOR YOU BEING HERE, ALL MEMORIES OF THIS PLACE, AFTER SEEING THEM DIE...

THANKFULLY, I NEVER SAW IT... BUT HEARING THEIR SCREAMS WAS ENOUGH. I REALIZED WHAT WAS HAPPENING AND RAN. I GUESS I DIDN'T REALIZE THAT I WAS *LEAVING* THEM.

MAYBE IF I HAD GONE BACK, I COULD'VE DONE SOMETHING--

STOP. THERE IS NOTHING YOU COULD HAVE DONE. YOU ARE ALIVE NOW, AND NOT ONLY CAN YOU AVENGE THEM, BUT SAVE THEIR WORLD AS WELL.

HA! IF THERE EVER WAS A WORLD THAT NEEDED SAVING! POOR EIATTU! SO MANY DIRTY HANDS GROPING YOU!

PERHAPS COUNT LAABANN'S THE DIRTIEST OF ALL, EH?

NO QUESTION LAABANN IS A CONCERN TO OUR CAUSE. A HUTT TONGUE IS HARDLY AS SLIPPERY. HOWEVER, THE MAJORITY OF THE PRIAMSTA IS NOT AS FOOLISH. THEY WILL JOIN US.

AND WITH YOU LEADING US, WE WILL SURELY WIN THE DAY. I ONLY ASK THAT YOU ALLOW ME TO BE AT YOUR SIDE FROM NOW UNTIL THAT DAY COMES.

YOUR CONFIDENCE IN ME IS...REASSURING. I ONLY WISH THAT I COULD MATCH IT WITH MY OWN. I'VE FOUGHT SO MANY BATTLES, BUT THIS...

...IF THIS GOES WRONG, I'LL HAVE DESTROYED US ALL.

...AND THAT'S WHEN THE FIREWORKS STARTED!

THE IMPS MUST'VE LOST THE PLB IN THE SWAMPS, SO WHEN THEY SAW US WALKING UP, THEY STARTED BLASTING!

AND THAT'S WHEN YOU CALLED US.

--TO SAVE YOUR BUTTS!

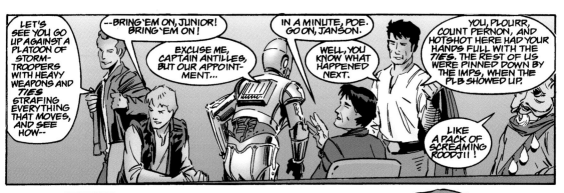

LET'S SEE YOU GO UP AGAINST A PLATOON OF STORM-TROOPERS WITH HEAVY WEAPONS AND TIES STRAFING EVERYTHING THAT MOVES, AND SEE HOW--

--BRING 'EM ON, JUNIOR! BRING 'EM ON!

EXCUSE ME, CAPTAIN ANTILLES, BUT OUR APPOINT-MENT...

IN A MINUTE, POE. GO ON, JANSON.

WELL, YOU KNOW WHAT HAPPENED NEXT.

YOU, PLOURR, COUNT PERNON, AND HOTSHOT HERE HAD YOUR HANDS FULL WITH THE TIES. THE REST OF US WERE PINNED DOWN BY THE IMPS, WHEN THE PLB SHOWED UP.

LIKE A PACK OF SCREAMING ROODJI!

THE NEXT THING WE KNEW, THE IMPS WERE ON THE RUN.

YEAH, IT WAS LIKE THEY REALIZED THEY SUDDENLY HAD SOMETHING SAFER TO DO!

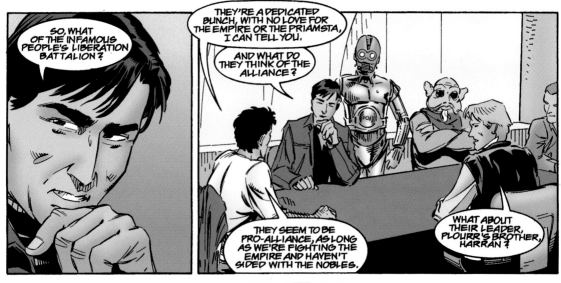

SO, WHAT OF THE INFAMOUS PEOPLE'S LIBERATION BATTALION?

THEY'RE A DEDICATED BUNCH, WITH NO LOVE FOR THE EMPIRE OR THE PRIAMSTA, I CAN TELL YOU.

AND WHAT DO THEY THINK OF THE ALLIANCE?

THEY SEEM TO BE PRO-ALLIANCE, AS LONG AS WE'RE FIGHTING THE EMPIRE AND HAVEN'T SIDED WITH THE NOBLES.

WHAT ABOUT THEIR LEADER, PLOURR'S BROTHER, HARRAN?

HE SEEMED TO HAVE THIS LIGHT AROUND HIM, AS THOUGH NOTHING IS IMPOSSIBLE WHEN HE'S AROUND. THE PLB REGULARS ARE READY TO HIT THE PRIMS HARD!

HE'S QUITE A MAN. HE HAS HIS TROOPS HIGHLY MOTIVATED AND READY FOR COMBAT.

AND HE'S A DEDICATED LEADER.

HE WAS OUT ALL NIGHT LOOKING FOR ONE OF HIS LOST TROOPS.

HE FINALLY FOUND HIM EARLY THIS MORNING. THE IMPS DIDN'T LEAVE MUCH.

SO, WHY DIDN'T YOU REPORT IN LAST NIGHT? SOME SORT OF IMP JAMMING?

NO. PLB JAMMING. SGT. ASHAAD, THE TROOPER WHO LED US BACK THIS MORNING, TOLD ME THAT THE PLB HAVE STATIC GENERATORS PLACED ALL AROUND THEIR CAMP.

AH, THAT WAY NEITHER THE PRIMS NOR THE IMPS CAN GET A FIX ON THEIR LOCATION.

SAY WEDGE, DID YOU GET AN EXIT VECTOR ON THOSE TIES THAT RAN OFF?

LOOKED TO ME LIKE THEY WENT DEEPER INTO THE SWAMPS, WHY?

BECAUSE THAT'S THE DIRECTION THE IMPS WENT WHEN THE PLB SHOWED UP.

RIDICULOUS! THE ONLY HOPE THIS WORLD HAS FOR PEACE AND ECONOMIC PROSPERITY RESTS WITH THE MONARCHY AND THE PRIAMSTA. THEY HAVE RULED THIS WORLD FOR GENERATIONS.

YES, BUT AT WHAT COST?! TIME AND TIME AGAIN, THE ROYAL CLASS HAS SOLD OUT ITS PEOPLE'S BLOOD AND SWEAT TO THE EMPIRE! HARRAN AND THE PLB ARE EIATTU'S ONLY CHANCE FOR THE NEW AGE OF FREEDOM!

I DON'T UNDERSTAND HOW YOU CAN DEFEND THE PRIMS, NRIN! LOOK AT THE DAMAGE THEY'VE CAUSED THE PLANET. THE NOBLE CLASS EVEN HAD A HAND IN THE DEATH OF PLOURR'S FAMILY! I THINK--

...HERE WE GO AGAIN...

THAT WAS A LONG TIME AGO, FEYLIS. THE PRIAMSTA TOTALLY DENOUNCES THEIR ACTION. THE VERY EXISTENCE OF THE PRIAMSTA IS TO ENSURE THAT NEVER HAPPENS AGAIN!

HOW CAN WE BE SO SURE THAT THOSE NOBLES WHO TOOK PART IN THE KILLINGS AREN'T MEMBERS OF THE PRIMS? WHY SHOULD PLOURR TRUST THEM?

SHE MUST, FOR THE GOOD OF THE ROYAL HOUSE! PLOURR MUST PLACE HER PERSONAL FEELINGS ASIDE!

LOOKS LIKE EVERYONE HAS AN OPINION ON THE SITUATION.

IT DOESN'T MAKE ANY SENSE FOR THE IMPS TO HEAD BACK INTO THE SWAMP--

--UNLESS THEY HAVE SOMETHING TO HIDE IN THERE!

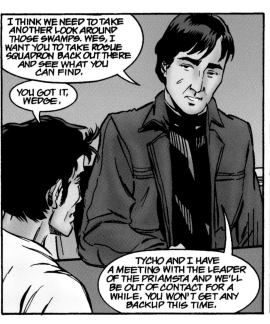

I THINK WE NEED TO TAKE ANOTHER LOOK AROUND THOSE SWAMPS. WES, I WANT YOU TO TAKE ROGUE SQUADRON BACK OUT THERE AND SEE WHAT YOU CAN FIND.

YOU GOT IT, WEDGE.

TYCHO AND I HAVE A MEETING WITH THE LEADER OF THE PRIAMSTA AND WE'LL BE OUT OF CONTACT FOR A WHILE. YOU WON'T GET ANY BACKUP THIS TIME.

DON'T WORRY, WEDGE. WE WON'T LET YOU DOWN.

I'VE GOT A GOOD FEELING ABOUT THIS ONE!

FIRST, GENTLEMEN, PLEASE ACCEPT MY MOST SINCERE APOLOGIES FOR MY OUTBURST LAST EVENING.

NO APOLOGIES NECESSARY, COUNT LAABANN, THERE ARE MANY STRONG OPINIONS IN THE EIATTU DEBATE.

INDEED... YOU ARE A MAN WHO UNDERSTANDS THE WAY OF THINGS, CAPTAIN ANTILLES. I SEE THIS IN YOU.

THANK YOU, COUNT LAABANN, BUT I'M SURE YOU DIDN'T ASK US HERE TO TRADE PLEASANTRIES.

AH, A MAN WHO DOES NOT WASTE WORDS. AN EXCELLENT TRAIT IN AN OFFICER.

WELL THEN, TO THE POINT OF THE MATTER.

I AM SURE, MY DEAR CAPTAIN, THAT YOU REALIZE THE IMPORTANCE OF EIATTU TO THE ALLIANCE. TRADE ROUTES, A FRIENDLY PORT... A WATCHFUL EYE OVER THE EMPIRE...

...HAVE YOU MEASURED THE GOALS OF THE ALLIANCE AND THOSE OF YOUR FORMER PILOT, OUR PRINCESS ISPLOURRDACARTHA?

I'M SURE THE ALLIANCE IS WILLING TO WORK WITH EIATTU, WHATEVER THE OUTCOME.

AH, BUT HAVE YOU CONSIDERED... DIRECTING THE OUTCOME TO YOUR OWN ADVANTAGE?

WITH YOU IN COMMAND OF ROGUE SQUADRON, COMBINED WITH MY PERSONAL HONOR GUARD OF HEADHUNTER FIGHTERS, WE COULD SECURE THE POLITICAL FUTURE OF THE PLANET.

WHAT!!?? TEAM UP WITH YOU AGAINST PLOURR??!! DON'T BET ON IT, YOU--

--EASY, TYCHO.

COUNT LAABANN, THAT WILL NEVER HAPPEN. THE ALLIANCE CANNOT AND WILL NOT TAKE SIDES IN THIS MATTER. WE--

CAPTAIN, SHOULD YOU NOT INFORM YOUR SUPERIORS OF MY OFFER?

I AM SURE THE LEADERS OF THE ALLIANCE REALIZE THAT THE SITUATION ON EIATTU IS A FLUID ONE. ONE MUST BE PREPARED TO BEND,...AS THE RIVER CHANGES COURSE THROUGH THE LAND.

AND WHO KNOWS, PERHAPS OUR NEWLY FOUND PRINCESS MAY JUST DECIDE TO DISAPPEAR ONCE AGAIN.

PLOURR IS A BIG GIRL, SHE CAN TAKE CARE OF HERSELF. I THINK YOU'LL FIND HER TO BE MORE THAN ENOUGH TO HANDLE.

BUT IF YOU WANT TO TRY ME AS WELL?

YOU'RE MAKING WAGERS THAT YOUR NOBILITY CAN'T HONOR.

POE, THE DOOR.

VERY GOOD, SIR.

DAMN THAT REBEL UPSTART.

THE PLB OR THE PRIAMSTA, THESE ARE THE ALLIES I HAVE TO CHOOSE FROM? AT LEAST I KNOW WHERE THE EMPIRE STANDS!

I KNOW YOU WILL MAKE THE RIGHT CHOICE.

OH? AND JUST HOW DO YOU KNOW?

BECAUSE I KNOW YOU ...JUST AS EVERY HUSBAND SHOULD KNOW HIS WIFE.

I'M NOT YOUR WIFE !!!

YAAAAA!!!

I'M SORRY. BUT HOW CAN YOU CONTINUE TO HOLD ON TO THESE RIDICULOUS, ARCHAIC TRADITIONS?

WHAT IF I HAD BEEN DEAD ALL THESE YEARS, KILLED WITH MY FAMILY? WHO WOULD YOU LOVE THEN?

NO ONE. I WOULD HAVE DIED WITH YOU.

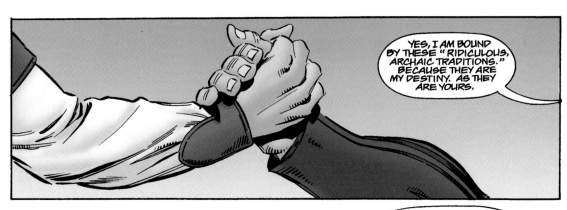

YES, I AM BOUND BY THESE "RIDICULOUS, ARCHAIC TRADITIONS." BECAUSE THEY ARE MY DESTINY. AS THEY ARE YOURS.

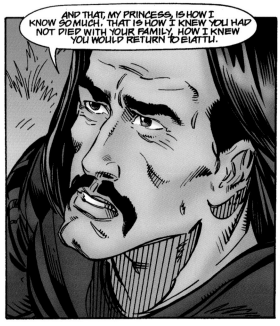

AND THAT, MY PRINCESS, IS HOW I KNOW SO MUCH. THAT IS HOW I KNEW YOU HAD NOT DIED WITH YOUR FAMILY, HOW I KNEW YOU WOULD RETURN TO EIATTU.

BECAUSE IT IS YOUR DESTINY TO RECLAIM THE THRONE...AND IT IS MY DESTINY TO BE AT YOUR SIDE WHEN YOU DO SO.

I DO LOVE YOU... AND I WILL MARRY YOU. AND I CAN SEE IN YOUR EYES THAT TRUTH IS DAWNING ON YOU.

WATCH YOUR SPACING, EVERYBODY. STAY SHARP.

HEY, DLLR, YOU HEAR ANYTHING YET?

WHAT?? NO, I DON'T HEAR A THING. SOMETHING'S WRONG WITH THIS PLACE, I TOLD YOU I HAD A VERY BAD--

OWWWW!!! WWW!!! OOO

DLLR, WHAT'S WRONG?!

DLLR, ARE YOU OKAY?

YEAH, I THINK SO. FELT LIKE SOMEONE WAS TRYING TO SLIP A VIBROBLADE THROUGH MY HEAD!

CAN YOU MAKE IT? WE COULD--

--I'M FINE, LET'S MOVE ON. MY HEAD'S CLEARING NOW.

WELL, I'LL BE-- JANSON, I THINK YOU'D BETTER SEE THIS.

WHAT IS THAT?

I'VE GOT AN IDEA, IF YOU'LL ALLOW ME TO DO THE HONORS?

LOOKS LIKE THEY FOUND ONE, THEY'RE ALL IN POSITION, GET READY.

JUST AS I SUSPECTED. IT'S A GRAY NOISE GENERATOR. DEFINITELY AN IMPERIAL DEVICE.

GREAT.

BUT WHY? AND WHY DID IT AFFECT DLLR AND NOT US?

IT'S USED TO BAFFLE THE NOISE OF LARGE MACHINES WHEN YOU DON'T WANT TO BE HEARD. DLLR'S INCREDIBLE HEARING WAS ABLE TO PICK UP THE PULSE IT SENDS OUT--

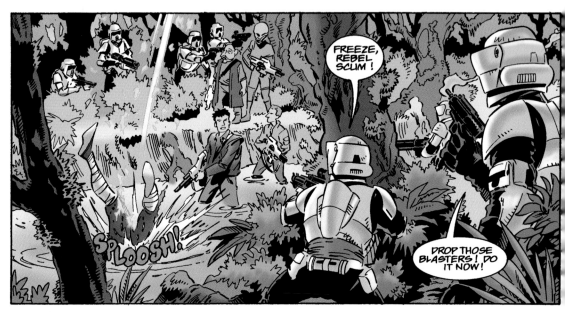

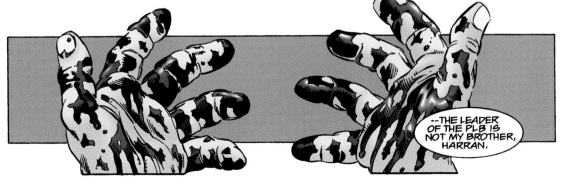

...ON THAT NIGHT, I KILLED MY LITTLE BROTHER, HARRAN, WITH MY OWN HANDS--

--AND I'D DO IT AGAIN.

BUT, HOW? WHY?

YOU, OF ALL PEOPLE, SHOULD HAVE SUSPECTED, RIAL. YOU KNEW WHAT PRINCE HARRAN WAS. YOU KNEW THE ROYAL FAMILY'S DIRTY LITTLE SECRET.

WHAT DO YOU MEAN, PLOURR?

I MEAN THAT EVEN IN PARADISE, THERE IS ALWAYS THE TOUCH OF EVIL.

"THE BLOOD LINE OF MY FAMILY HAS BEEN KEPT PERFECT FOR OVER TEN GENERATIONS BY THE ROYAL LIFE-ENGINES. EIATTU'S FINEST SCIENTISTS WERE CHARGED WITH ACHIEVING WHAT NATURE COULD NOT...

"...KEEPING THE GENETIC LINE PURE, CLEAR OF ALL THE ILLS THAT PLAGUE THE CITIZENS OF EIATTU. BUT AS YOU KNOW, NATURE ABHORS A VACUUM.

"AND AS SURE AS EIATTU REVOLVES AROUND THE SUN, MY LITTLE BROTHER, PRINCE HARRANDATHA WAS MAD.

"ALL THOSE YEARS OF DIPPING FROM THE SAME GENETIC POOL CAUSED A WRINKLE, A FLAW IN AN OTHERWISE NORMAL FAMILY LINE.

"YET IT WAS NEVER SPOKEN OF ALOUD....ONLY IN THE DARK CORRIDORS OF THE PALACE, GOSSIPED BY KITCHEN MAIDS AND ROYAL PHYSICIANS.

"THERE WAS ONLY ONE THING THAT GAVE MY BROTHER MORE PLEASURE THAN THE SUFFERING OF OTHERS WEAKER THAN HIMSELF.

"THE EMPIRE, AND ITS CHAMPION, DARTH VADER, DARK LORD OF THE SITH.

" I SUPPOSE MY PARENTS SHOULD HAVE EXPECTED IT.

" WE SET OUT TO KEEP OURSELVES ABOVE THE COMMON MAN AND FOUND OURSELVES WITH A THING FROM THE DEEPEST PIT OF THE SITH.

" THE DAY VADER CAME TO EIATTU HIMSELF TO INSPECT THE IMPERIAL GARRISON AND TO VISIT WITH HIS GREATEST ADMIRER, WAS THE HAPPIEST DAY OF MY BROTHER'S LIFE."

"THEY PLAYED IN HARRAN'S ROOM FOR HOURS.

"NO ONE WAS ALLOWED INTO THE ROOM AND NO ONE KNOWS WHAT THEY TALKED ABOUT.

"BUT WHEN THEY FINALLY WALKED OUT, SOMETHING IN HARRAN HAD CHANGED. IT WAS AS IF THE MEETING WITH VADER HAD PURGED THE DARKNESS INSIDE OF HARRA AND REPLACED IT WITH SOMETHING ELSE

"SOMETHING COLD.

"MY PARENTS WERE RELIEVED.

"THAT IS, UNTIL THAT NIGHT, THE NIGHT I RAN AWAY.

"MY FATHER WAS ABLE TO LIFT ME TO A VENTING SHAFT THAT LED TO THE OUTSIDE.

"THERE WAS ONLY ONE THING STOPPING ME.

"MY DARLING LITTLE BROTHER,

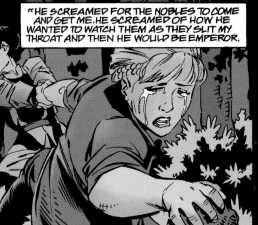

"HE SCREAMED FOR THE NOBLES TO COME AND GET ME. HE SCREAMED OF HOW HE WANTED TO WATCH THEM AS THEY SLIT MY THROAT AND THEN HE WOULD BE EMPEROR.

"HIS SCREAMS MIXED WITH THE SCREAMS OF MY FAMILY AS THEY WERE PUT TO DEATH, AND THERE WAS ONLY ONE THING I WANTED TO DO.

"PUT AN END TO THE SCREAMING."

"I DRAGGED HIS BODY INTO THE BRUSH, IT DIDN'T TAKE LONG FOR A PACK OF THUVASAURS TO PICK UP THE SCENT."

PRINCESS...

PLOURR...IF THE LEADER OF THE PLB IS NOT YOUR BROTHER, THEN WHO IS HE?

YOU CAN BET HE'S AN IMPERIAL SPY.

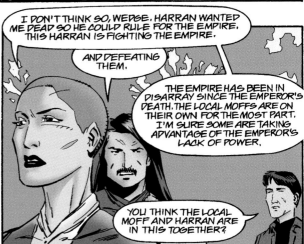

I DON'T THINK SO, WEDGE. HARRAN WANTED ME DEAD SO HE COULD RULE FOR THE EMPIRE. THIS HARRAN IS FIGHTING THE EMPIRE.

AND DEFEATING THEM.

THE EMPIRE HAS BEEN IN DISARRAY SINCE THE EMPEROR'S DEATH. THE LOCAL MOFFS ARE ON THEIR OWN FOR THE MOST PART. I'M SURE SOME ARE TAKING ADVANTAGE OF THE EMPEROR'S LACK OF POWER.

YOU THINK THE LOCAL MOFF AND HARRAN ARE IN THIS TOGETHER?

IF I KNOW MOFF TAVIRA, SHE IS BEHIND THIS ENTIRE CHARADE. I--

WHAT THE--!?

TIE FIGHTERS!

IT LOOKS AS IF THE PLB HAS DECIDED TO START THE REVOLUTION!

THEY'RE STORMING THE IMPERIAL CITADEL! IMPOSTOR OR NO IMPOSTOR, HE'S NOT GOING TO BURN DOWN MY CITY! LET'S GET TO THE HANGARS!

IF THE IMPS ARE FIGHTING FOR THE PLB, WHO'S IN THE SWAMP WITH ROGUE SQUADRON?!!

LET'S HIT 'EM HARD!

FOR THE PRIDE OF EIATTU!

KROOM!

NO YOU DON'T, YOU LITTLE--

VRRAPP!

VRRAPP!

THANK THE STARS!

WEDGE, WE'VE GOT TO TAKE OUT THAT TURBOLASER!

I'LL BE--

NO... NOT AGAIN.

ALL THIS TIME LOOKING FOR A REBEL CORPSE! WE'LL NEVER FIND IT IN THIS MUD HOLE!

WE'D BETTER. DID YOU HEAR WHAT SHE DID TO LT. VOLKS FOR NOT BRINGING THE BODY BACK?

NO, WHAT'D SHE DO?

I DON'T KNOW WHAT YOU CALL IT, BUT IT WASN'T PRETTY.

BLOOOPPP BLOPPP... BLIPPP

WHAT THE--

HEY, YOU BETTER WATCH IT. WHO KNOWS WHAT'S SWIMMING AROUND IN THAT MUCK.

YAAAAA!!!

DEVERS!!!

DEVERS???

DEV--

KRAKKK!

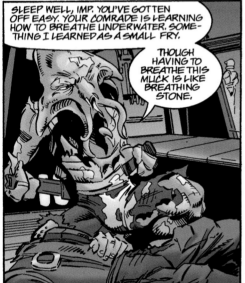

SLEEP WELL, IMP. YOU'VE GOTTEN OFF EASY. YOUR COMRADE IS LEARNING HOW TO BREATHE UNDERWATER. SOMETHING I LEARNED AS A SMALL FRY.

THOUGH HAVING TO BREATHE THIS MUCK IS LIKE BREATHING STONE.

THEY MUST HAVE TAKEN THE OTHERS TO THIS LOCATION. WELL, I THINK THEY'RE IN FOR A LITTLE SURPRISE.

YOU THERE! DON'T MOVE!

UH, OH. TIME TO GO!

ROGUE SQUADRON, HERE I COME! YEEEEHAAAAA!

VRAPPP!

VRAPPP!

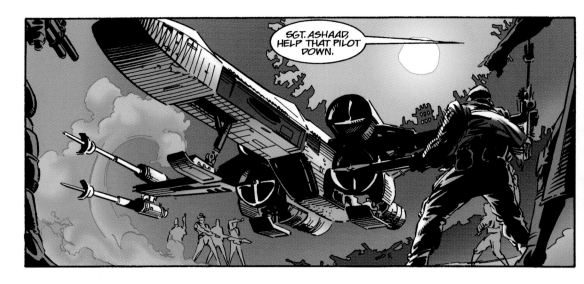

THIS MAN IS AN IMPOSTOR! A PLANT TO CREATE UNREST BETWEEN THE NOBLES AND THE CITIZENS OF EIATTU!

THE TRUE HARRAN DIED YEARS AGO ON THE NIGHT MY FAMILY WAS MURDERED!

HOW DO YOU KNOW THIS, SISTER DEAR? HOW DO YOU KNOW THAT I WAS KILLED THAT HORRIBLE NIGHT?

BECAUSE *I* KILLED YOU!

PRINCE HARRAN WAS MAD! AN ABOMINATION, CREATED FROM YEARS OF GENETIC TAMPERING!

PRINCE HARRAN WAS ALSO AN IMPERIAL SPY, CORRUPTED BY DARTH VADER HIMSELF!

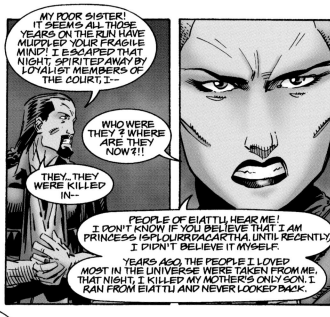

MY POOR SISTER! IT SEEMS ALL THOSE YEARS ON THE RUN HAVE MUDDLED YOUR FRAGILE MIND! I ESCAPED THAT NIGHT, SPIRITED AWAY BY LOYALIST MEMBERS OF THE COURT, I--

WHO WERE THEY? WHERE ARE THEY NOW?!!

THEY... THEY WERE KILLED IN--

PEOPLE OF EIATTU, HEAR ME! I DON'T KNOW IF YOU BELIEVE THAT I AM PRINCESS ISPLOURRDACARTHA. UNTIL RECENTLY, I DIDN'T BELIEVE IT MYSELF.

YEARS AGO, THE PEOPLE I LOVED MOST IN THE UNIVERSE WERE TAKEN FROM ME. THAT NIGHT, I KILLED MY MOTHER'S ONLY SON. I RAN FROM EIATTU AND NEVER LOOKED BACK.

NOW I KNOW THAT YOU CAN NEVER RUN FROM YOUR HOME. EIATTU IS THE BIRTHWORLD OF MY FATHER AND MOTHER, OF MY ENTIRE FAMILY. EIATTU TOOK EVERYTHING I HAD AWAY FROM ME, YES.

BUT IT GAVE EVERYTHING TO ME, AS WELL. AND ALL THOSE THINGS, MY FAMILY AND THEIR LOVE ARE HERE, IN EVERY BLADE OF GRASS, IN ALL THE ROLLING HILLS,...

...AND IN YOU GOOD PEOPLE.

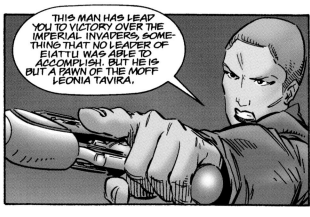

THIS MAN HAS LEAD YOU TO VICTORY OVER THE IMPERIAL INVADERS, SOMETHING THAT NO LEADER OF EIATTU WAS ABLE TO ACCOMPLISH. BUT HE IS BUT A PAWN OF THE MOFF LEONIA TAVIRA.

LIES....

LIES!! I CAME BACK TO THIS PLANET TO SAVE MY PEOPLE FROM THE OPPRESSION OF THE NOBLES! TO BRING ABOUT A NEW AGE TO OUR WORLD.

WHAT HAS *SHE* DONE BUT CODDLE THE PRIAMSTA AND THE IMPERIALS!

I LED YOU PEOPLE TO VICTORY! I--

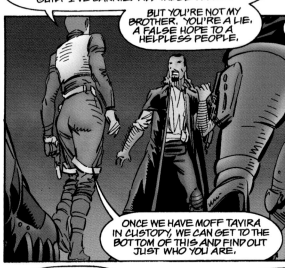

--I ALMOST WISH THAT YOU WERE MY BROTHER, AT LEAST THEN I WOULD NOT HAVE TO LIVE WITH THE GUILT I'VE CARRIED ALL THESE YEARS.

BUT YOU'RE NOT MY BROTHER. YOU'RE A LIE, A FALSE HOPE TO A HELPLESS PEOPLE.

ONCE WE HAVE MOFF TAVIRA IN CUSTODY, WE CAN GET TO THE BOTTOM OF THIS AND FIND OUT JUST WHO YOU ARE.

GET BACK! SGT. ASHAAD, STOP HER!

B-BUT, MY LORD...

YOU SEE, THESE PEOPLE DON'T NEED US.

THIS IS THE STRENGTH OF EIATTU, NOT ITS LEADERS. ITS STRENGTH LIES IN ITS PEOPLE.

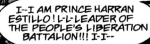

I SAID STAY BACK!!! STOP HER!!!

I--I AM PRINCE HARRAN ESTILLO! L-L-LEADER OF THE PEOPLE'S LIBERATION BATTALION!!! I-I--

AND THAT RING, "BROTHER DEAR," JUST ISN'T YOU!

PLOURR, ARE YOU ALL RIGHT?

YES, RIAL, I'M FINE.

WE VAPED THE LAST OF THE *TIES*. THE CITADEL IS SECURE.

SO, THIS IS THE WOULD-BE PRINCE.

WEDGE, HAVE YOU HEARD FROM JANSON AND THE OTHERS?

I JUST GOT WORD FROM HIM. HE AND THE REST OF ROGUE SQUADRON WERE THE UNWILLING GUESTS OF THE MOFF.

"JANSON TOLD ME THAT THEY MANAGED TO ESCAPE WITH A LITTLE HELP FROM NRIN. IT SEEMS THAT MOFF TAVIRA WAS ABLE TO ESCAPE WITH ONLY A PORTION OF THE ROYAL FUNDS SHE HAD STOLEN.

"THEY WERE ABLE TO RESCUE THE REST OF IT AND ARE WAITING FOR YOU TO SEND A TRANSPORT TO THEIR LOCATION. "

WHAT ABOUT HIM?

AND WHAT ABOUT THE PLB? WHAT ABOUT COUNT LAABANN AND THE PRIAMSTA? WHO WILL RULE EIATTU?

WE'LL CARE FOR HIM THE BEST WE CAN, UNTIL WE CAN FIND OUT JUST WHAT WAS DONE TO HIM.

AND AS FOR THE REST...

ARE YOU SURE YOU WON'T JOIN US, PLOURR? THERE'S STILL TIME, YOU KNOW.

I APPRECIATE THAT, BUT MY DUTY IS... MY LIFE IS HERE.

THIS WORLD BORE ME. NOW, *SHE* DESPERATELY NEEDS TO BE NURSED BACK TO STRENGTH.

PERHAPS AFTER THAT, WITH NEWFOUND UNITY, WE CAN THEN LEARN TO WALK TOGETHER.

"REGARDLESS OF WHERE THOSE STEPS MAY TAKE US, THE ACTIONS OF CERTAIN PARTIES WILL NOT BE FORGOTTEN."

EVEN THOUGH MOFF TAVIRA GOT AWAY WITH A FAIR AMOUNT OF IMPERIAL BULLION, WE'LL DO OUR BEST TO TRACK HER DOWN FOR YOU--

NO NEED TO CONCERN YOURSELF WITH THAT. THE MAJORITY OF THE FUNDS ARE STILL IN MY POSSESSION.

WHAT ABOUT THE IMPOSTOR? WHAT HAPPENS TO HIM NOW?

THE POOR SOUL...

"WHATEVER MIND HE MAY HAVE POSSESSED BEFORE, EITHER HARRAN'S OR HIS OWN...

"...IS GONE NOW."

AS FAR AS OUR RESEARCHERS CAN DETERMINE, THE RING HE WORE WAS SOME KIND OF BRAIN-PROGRAMMING DEVICE.

CONTACT WITH IT SOMEHOW REINFORCED THE REAL HARRAN'S MEMORIES THAT HAD BEEN IMPLANTED INTO HIS MIND.

THE VERY IDEA OF SUCH A DEVICE IS UNMISTAKABLY VADER.

DESTROYING THE DEVICE AS I DID MAY HAVE ERASED HIS MIND, BUT AT LEAST HE IS FREE OF THE EMPIRE'S INFLUENCE.

OUR PHYSICIANS WILL CARE FOR HIM AS BEST THEY CAN.

Michael A. Stackpole

Michael A. Stackpole is an award-winning game designer and novelist who earned a BA in History from the University of Vermont in 1979, which directly contributed to the production of *The Warrior Princess* by giving him the background information on the last Tsar of Russia and the fate of his family, which Mike warped into this story. Best known for his series of X-Wing novels, his most recent *Star Wars* novel is *I, Jedi*, and he has collaborated with Timothy Zahn on a new *Star Wars* project for Dark Horse Comics: the *Mara Jade* mini-series.

Scott Tolson

"In June of 1977, two things would happen to me that would change my life forever: I bought my first comic book, and a week later I saw *Star Wars*. In an instant, I knew exactly what I wanted to do when I grew up — get bitten by a radioactive spider and fly an X-Wing. Twenty years later, I have yet to be bitten by that spider, but I did get to command a whole squadron of X-Wings. And, man, it was cool!"

Scott works as an illustrator and scriptwriter in the Seattle area. *The Warrior Princess* is the third project Scott has scripted for Dark Horse, his former work including the acclaimed 1995 Spike Lee/Dark Horse Comics miniseries *Colors in Black*.

John Nadeau and Jordi Ensign

John Nadeau is an out of work Cybernetics Engineer on the run from government agents determined to squelch his brilliant research. John chose comic-book art as a suitably low-key underground occupation and constructed Jordi Ensign, a human-like cybernetic organism, to ink his techno-based comic books.

Jordi Ensign (Omega Series VI construct, designate "Jordster," aka "Jordi-Grrl") was initially designed as a college thesis project. Her current primary function is to ink her creator's complex tech-creations, but she also serves as a bodyguard (she once punched through a plate-glass window, shattering it without suffering a scratch) and chauffeur to John, keeping him out of harm's way at all times.

John and Jordi are an explosive combination and should be approached with extreme caution. They have successfully eluded government agents by basing their operations in an as-yet undiscovered Orlando suburb.

STAR WARS
X-WING
ROGUE SQUADRON

the warrior princess

GALLERY

Featuring the original

comic-book series

cover paintings by

Mark Harrison

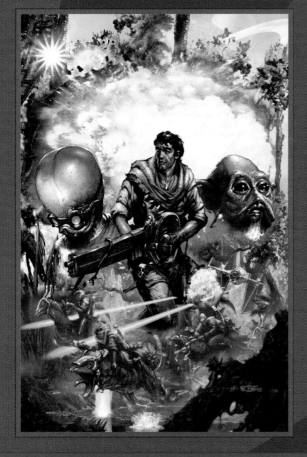

ALIENS

FEMALE WAR
(formerly *Aliens: Earth War*)
Verheiden • Kieth
112-page color paperback
ISBN: 1-85286-784-1 £11.99

GENOCIDE
Arcudi • Willis • Story
112-page color paperback
ISBN: 1-85286-805-8 £10.99

LABYRINTH
Woodring • Plunkett
136-page color paperback
ISBN: 1-85286-844-9 £11.99

NIGHTMARE ASYLUM
(formerly *Aliens: Book Two*)
Verheiden • Beauvais
112-page color paperback
ISBN: 1-85286-765-5 £11.99

NEWT'S TALE
Richardson • Somerville • Garvey
96-page color paperback
ISBN: 1-85286-575-x £6.99

ROGUE
Edginton • Simpson
112-page color paperback
ISBN: 1-85286-838-4 £11.99

HARVEST
(formerly *Aliens: Hive*)
Prosser • Jones
112-page color paperback
ISBN: 1-85286-838-4 £11.99

OUTBREAK
(formerly *Aliens: Book One*)
Verheiden • Nelson
168-page B&W paperback
ISBN: 1-85286-756-6 £11.99

STRONGHOLD
Arcudi • Mahnke • Palmiotti
112-page color paperback
ISBN: 1-85286-875-9 £11.99

ALIENS VS PREDATOR

ALIENS VS PREDATOR
Stradley • Warner
176-page color paperback
ISBN: 1-85286-413-3 £10.99

DEADLIEST OF THE SPECIES
Claremont • Guice • Barreto
320-page color paperback
ISBN: 1-85286-953-4 £19.99

WAR
Stradley • Warner
200-page color paperback
ISBN: 1-85286-703-5 £12.99

GODZILLA

AGE OF MONSTERS
various
256-page B&W paperback
ISBN: 1-85286-929-1 £10.99

PAST PRESENT FUTURE
various
276-page B&W paperback
ISBN: 1-85286-930-5 £10.99

PREDATOR

BIG GAME
Arcudi • Dorkin • Gil
112-page color paperback
ISBN: 1-85286-454-0 £7.50

COLD WAR
Verheiden • Randall • Mitchell
112-page color paperback
ISBN: 1-85286-576-8 £8.99

KINDRED
Lamb • Tolsonl
112-page color paperback
ISBN: 1-85286-908-9 £9.99

All publications are available through most good bookshops or direct from our mail-order service at Titan Books. For a free graphic novels catalogue or to order, telephone 01536 763 631 with your credit-card details or contact Titan Books Mail Order PO Box 54, Desborough, Northants., NN14 2UH, quoting reference SW/GA.